G000166301

Michael Viney's **Natural World**

For Ethna

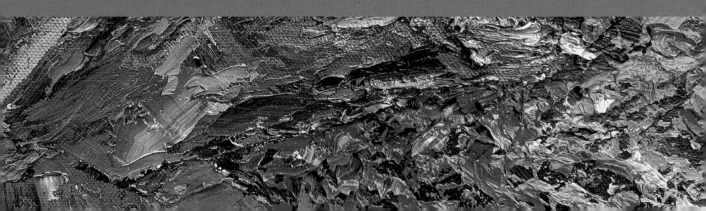

Michael Viney's Natural World

Foreword by Michael Longley

ARTISAN HOUSE PUBLISHING

Books of *taste* Created with *passion* In the heart of *Connemara*

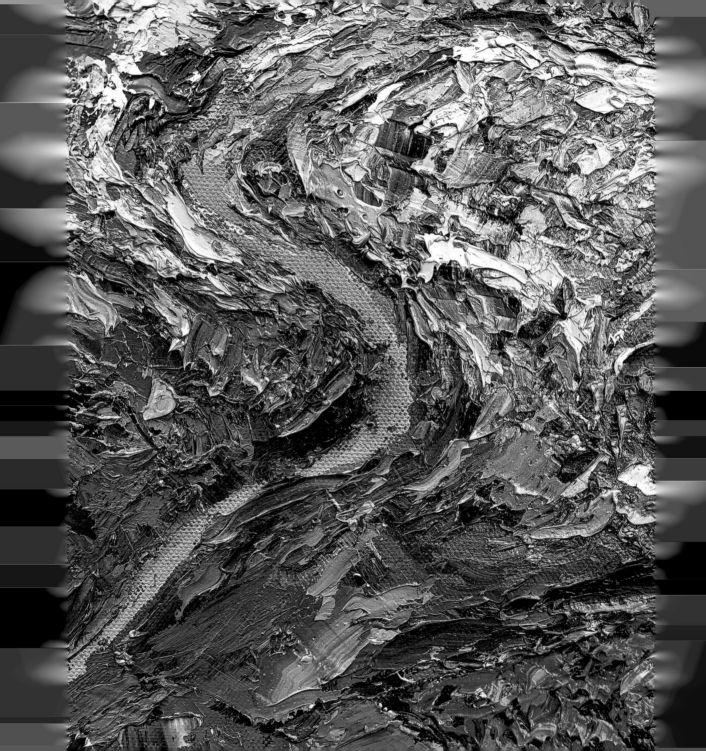

Michael Longley Foreword

Way back in the early 1970s when I was first falling
under the Mayo spell, a mutual friend led me to
believe that Michael Viney preferred to be left alone
in his Thallabawn retreat. He in turn was under the
impression that I should never be disturbed amid
the silence of Carrigskeewaun. So, for some time, we
circled each other nervously, eager to avoid desecrating
one another's creative solitude. Eventually I called at
his cottage to buy some home-made cheese.
The rapport was instantaneous, profound and lasting.

To begin with, we are inspired by the same landscape.
In 1977 Michael and his wife Ethna and daughter
Michele moved from Dublin to their 'thorn-edged
acre' in Thallabawn on the Mayo coast. And I, every
year since 1970, have journeyed with my family from
Belfast to the neighbouring townland of Carrigskeewaun,
the guest of our dear friend and occasional collaborator,
the great ornithologist David Cabot.

Doo Lough Michael Viney *c* 2003 (detail)

Michael and I have walked together along the great yellow strand to Allaran Point to look for otter tracks, or up the hill behind his home to a big tarn called Lough Cunnel, or around Mweelrea mountain to the deserted village of Derry, or through fences to the ferny, lichen-draped oak woods at Old Head, or to Brackloon below Croagh Patrick. At precisely the right time I have stood beside him and watched the sun rolling down the side of the Reek, a ball of fire.

More usually I have followed in his footsteps as a reader, a student of his marvellous communiqués from the west, eager for news of his tiny smallholding and the windy world beyond its snug maze of fuchsia hedges. Michael's gaze reached from his compost heap to the Milky Way, from his own lovingly tended potato crop to the overgrown lazy beds with their Famine ghosts across the ridge, from yesterday's weather all the way back to the ice age.

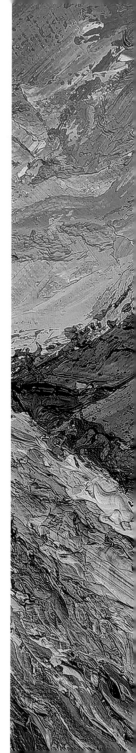

Once in a while Michael and I shared more private
thoughts – for instance, what's going to happen to us
when we die, a question that for both of us might best
be answered in terms of our shared soul-landscape,
and therefore with joyfulness as well as trepidation.
Michael helped me towards half an answer, perhaps.
My poem 'Petalwort' is dedicated to him:

There's no such place as heaven, so let it be
The Carriknashinnagh shoal or Cahir
Island where you honeymooned in a tent
Amid the pilgrim-fishermen's stations,

Your spillet disentangling and trailing off
Into the night, a ghost on every hook – dab
And flounder, thorny skate – at ebb tide you
Kneeling on watery sand to haul them in.

Early on in this book Michael recalls seeing his first otter 'framed in the emerald window of a wave'. That incandescent image encapsulates his vision and practice. His vocabulary seems to have been born out of the locale itself: 'cool fleeces of dead-nettle and jostling chickweed'. Phrases abound that any poet would envy – the corncrake's 'ratchety mantras'; 'mist hanging to the mountain like fungus'; 'the tattle of the stream'; 'an inky rim of cloud'. This is writing of the utmost distinction, wild and wonderful. Even when he is explaining complicated scientific facts, Michael's utterance is sustained by a lovely verbal melody. He enjoys perfect pitch.

Very recently, in an attempt to order my midden of papers, I discovered from twenty-three years ago a smudgy photocopy of a stunning short article by Michael about Thallabawn strand. It took my breath away and spontaneously arranged itself as a 'found poem'. For me, found poems are part of poetry's mystery. If they work, why do they work? I called my newfound poem

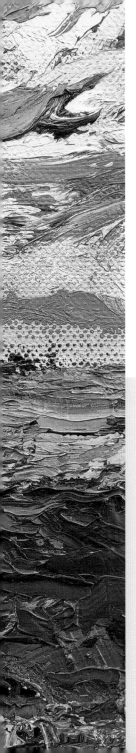

'Viney's Immortality' and, anxious as to how he might respond to my borrowing, I sent it to its only begetter. This was *his* gift to me, I said, and *my* gift to him, ultimate reciprocity, spiritual conversation, soul- companionship. 'Remarkable and magical,' he responded, 'like a special piece of driftwood.' Relieved and happy, I felt that we were walking again on the strand, beachcombing side by side along the tide-line:

VINEY'S IMMORTALITY

Your ashes will settle
With instant self-effacement
Into Thallabawn strand
At the foot of the hill,
Sifting among the fragments
Of other worn-out lives,
Tiny scallop fans in pink
And orange, minute cowries
Like rolled-up fingerprints,

Curved tiles from the broken
Domes of sea-urchins
Violet and rose, and here
A broody ringed plover
Nestling down to lay her eggs,
Enfolding crumbs of your skull,
Michael, into the warmth
Of her white breast-feathers.

In later years Michael retired as the baker of a
reliable crusty loaf, and Ethna no longer brewed
her fragrant home-made wines. They gave up
climbing the hill to save turf, and instead burned
wood in a cosy Scandinavian stove. They sold their
currach. Where have their lobster pots gone? They
didn't get up at dawn any more to beat the gulls to
spillet-hooked fish. Báinín the Connemara pony

found a friendly home elsewhere. Hens and ducks were happy memories. Meg I and Meg II, tubby, busy, brown-eyed mongrels, were not replaced.

The particulars and episodes which Michael commemorated so lovingly in his peerless chronicle *Another Life* now light up in vivid retrospect *Michael Viney's Natural World*. Michael shared his locale with the world while at the same time accommodating the world's marvels. Born to write, born to draw and paint (his 'dark kaleidoscope'), this deep-souled creator reconciled poetry and science. His lifetime's work, his Mayo adventure by the sea, has been culturally of the greatest moment. For myself, the name Viney rings out with the sandpiper's peep from marram grass, or the ravens' overhead conversation, or the curlews' keening beside the lake at evening.

Michael Longley *May 2023*

Doo Lough Michael Viney *c* 2003 Oil on canvas, application by palette knife.

Into the west

By the time I first headed west, in October 1961, Connemara had cleared up after Debbie, the worst Irish hurricane in years. Toppled trees were logged and stacked, shattered slates swept off the road, shreds of toppled haystacks fed to cattle. Cycling towards the mountains, I faced into a clean and reasonable breeze.

The bike had come with me from London, and more would follow: a chest of books and the radio, a painter's easel. I was having my year's sabbatical and then I'd see. After eager teens and twenties in Brighton home-town journalism, Fleet Street had let me down. 'Forget politics,' said the cable as I waited for President Nasser in Cairo, 'want belly-dancers.' The magazine suddenly had a new editor, of tabloid taste. I looked to see how much I'd saved in the bank, and at twenty-eight there wasn't very much. But where I was headed, a big mutton curry might be made to last a week.

The cottage in Connemara sat in a hillside hollow of the Renvyle peninsula where the village street of Tully began. It had, perhaps, been in better shape in 1929 when, on recent diary evidence, the nineteen-year-old Francis Bacon set up his very first studio in one of the better-lit rooms. He was there on a rare family holiday and found the beds a bit damp. In the wake of Hurricane Debbie, I could have found the same.

Across the road was a corner store with a side of bacon on the counter and beyond the hanging buckets a brief bar for pints of stout and a hatch for selling stamps. The store looked down to the shore, where the small, granite, post-Famine pier was left dry at low tide, and then out across the wide mouth of Ireland's one big fiord to Mweelrea, the highest peak in Connacht.

At the foot of the mountain a bright line of sand caught the sun. My eye was drawn to it, so remote and promisingly pristine. It was where, as things turned out, I would spend the last half of my life.

Mweelrea ridge

I did not return to Britain after the year, but sold my bike, headed to Dublin and petitioned the *Irish Times*. The new national mood was positive, and the newspaper had room for an outsider. We became partners, for the next sixty years.

The pull of the wilder landscape was, however, slow to ease. At weekends I took buses into Wicklow for walks in the hills. On New Year's Eve of 1962 I took a long, incautious and solitary hike from Roundwood, over a snow-carpeted Lugnaquilla Mountain. I remember the ankle-deep crunch of my boots across the summit, and the shock of bare curves in the landscape beyond. Plodding down the valley to catch the last bus from Baltinglass, I arrived, a lucky innocent, in the first flakes of Ireland's heaviest blizzard in years.

In 1965, with a three-week holiday in prospect, I embarked on what I hoped would be an ultimate experience of Irish landscape. From a map of County Kerry's Blasket Islands, I picked Inishvickillane, next to the open Atlantic. Robin Flower was there once, to catch rabbits, and felt it 'inhabited with the sense of loneliness: it is as though it were at the last end of things, dwelling in a silence which the ceaseless murmur of the sea around its base and the whining gulls about its summit rather accentuate than disturb'.

Cast away in September by lobster-boat from Dingle, I pitched a tent in the lee of a solitary stone cottage, deserted by the Ó Dalaigh family in the 1950s. Its tarred roof was drooping and bound down with cables, and a small, stone sundial marked its shadow outside the door. It was there to greet a taoiseach, Charles Haughey, with grander plans, when he bought the island in 1974.

I was a young Romantic, and it showed here and there in the diary I kept for a series in the *Irish Times*. ('The sun set red tonight and I watched it all the way down, smoking a last pipe and listening to the Beethoven violin concerto,' or, 'I crawled from the sleeping bag as from a chrysalis and stretched in the sun. Suddenly properly hungry for the first time in days, I hacked thick slices off the slab of bacon and played Vivaldi's "Le Printemps" while they sizzled...' I had eight hours of cassettes and twenty hours of batteries, so there was rather a lot of this.) I doubt if Haughey ever stewed a rabbit on a fire of dried sheep dung or had a grey seal snatch a pollack off his spinner. But, with a glass of good claret in his hand, he must have known those incredible evenings when, as I wrote, 'a theatrical clarity of light lent the islands new perspectives: deep avenues of cliffs like vistas in a Piranesi, gleaming and gold-enamelled (slow bursts of spun-glass spray).'

Bird's eye view

*The last end of things
on Inishvickillane*

Grey seal

The island was rarely silent and certainly not in the summer storm that on the sixth day and night wrapped me in a rain-sodden tent. The island's cliffs were ringed with vocal puffins, guillemots and the rest, but its stone walls offered the most intriguing calls of all – the churring chicks of storm petrels. The gale's gusts had made me move the tent to better shelter, but while this brought me closer to the petrels' hidden nests, it did not occur to me that I might be in their way. Thus, around midnight, I was shocked awake as a succession of petrels returning from the sea struck the canvas over my head and slithered down it.

Peering out, I found the night sky scissored with little black wings, like those of bats. It also echoed with weirdly cackling, screeching calls – these not from the petrels but from Manx shearwaters, their much bigger cousins, also flying in to their burrows with food. It was an awesome and disquieting, if privileged, introduction to Ireland's most precious seabirds. With nocturnal schedules to protect them from predatory skuas and gulls, the remoter, undisturbed islands off the UK and Ireland host the bulk of their global breeding populations.

My Inishvickillane adventure proved even more momentous: it prompted my girlfriend to sail out to rescue me. Worried by the storm, Ethna had driven to Dingle to find that the town's maritime workforce was attending a Sunday football match, including the boat owner scheduled to point me back to my desk. Enlisting a friendly trawler skipper, she volunteered as crew and, at the island, held the wheel of the small trawler steady below the cliffs while the skipper rowed in to take me off. I remember her blonde pony tail, triumphant at the tiller.

We were wed months later, in a marriage that kept the west of Ireland as part of life. Reared in Westport and a graduate in economics, Ethna was devoted to co-operative action to 'save the west'. It brought us many weekend journeys from Dublin to meetings in small-town Connacht, most of them eventually fruitless.

But I had also married another lover of islands. We honeymooned on Clare Island in Clew Bay, serenaded by corncrakes, and where I saw my first otter, framed in the emerald window of a wave. For our first married holiday, we cast ourselves away on Caher, a small, uninhabited island between Inishturk and the mainland. On Sunday afternoons, with music wafting from our tent, the young men of 'Turk circled the cove, teasing us in their currachs. The buzz of outboard engines and the cries of discommoded lapwings were our concert's noises off.

We went on to camp in the windy maze of Inisheer's limestone walls, and on a cliff at High Island beside monastic ruins. It was there that, alarmed over discomfort after eating a lot of lobster, Ethna solicited a rapid return to the mainland, where a doctor unexpectedly diagnosed her pregnancy.

In 1977, with daughter Michele, we moved to Mayo for a midlife adventure in the skills of an 'alternative' lifestyle. This was chronicled in a weekly column for the *Irish Times* and in my book *A Year's Turning*. Life on a hillside acre brought entirely new experience of the natural world and a consuming fascination with its biodiversity. Like Michael Longley, the great poet and friend with whom I have shared this 'soul-landscape' for almost half a century, my first, awestruck view of it was from a curve in the narrow road above Thallabawn. The huge, wild arena, framed by mountains and the bay, has at its heart a large tongue of sand, backed by dunes, a grassy machair, the channel of the river from Mweelrea and lakes under shadowy cliffs.

A huge wide arena

Hillside at Thallabawn

Within all this, sheep grazed around a tiny farm bowered in sycamores, and fences marked out fields behind the shore, but little else in its sprawling scale showed any human hand. To reach the sands from our hillside acre, down the stony boreen to the shore, meant fording the little river from the mountain, at times just a rattling splash, at others a surging, impassable flood. A little way on, past drying furls of seaweed from the last spring tide, the flow from Mweelrea carved the long, curving channel to the sea. A crossing-place from the boreen to the sand was marked by a row of rocks, once set hopefully as stepping stones. More often I had to follow, sometimes in thigh boots, the shifting furrows of tractors taking feed across the channel.

Gleaming doorsteps of foam

For years, the screensaver on my computer has shown the strand on a sunny autumn morning, the sea calm for once and unfurling on the sand in slow, gleaming doorsteps of foam. Whatever the real weather on the shore below, it has offered an encouraging start to the day. It reminds me of early walks on the strand with my eyes closed, the sun a warm vermilion in their lids and the rustle of the waves on my right to keep me straight. For all but a handful of days in the year, there's no one else to bump into.

The few stones on this strand are scattered platters of green sandstone, carried in with the holdfasts of kelp wrenched up in winter storms. As wind scours the strand, the stones can be left balanced on stems of sand, like mushrooms. They are embossed with raised white hieroglyphs, the calcareous tubes of little seabed worms, and this bright rococo doodling made me gather enough to clad the chimney breast above the woodstove, a typically laborious endeavour of our early years at Thallabawn.

There was also, renewed twice a day, the winding tideline, a mortuary of fascinating flotsam, a museum of nature's other lives that were soon to mesmerise my own. Retrieved from anorak pockets, a jumble of sea urchins, crab shells, bird skulls, the vertebrae of dolphins and more, much more began to line our indoor window sills. A bowl of sea beans appeared, a staple trophy of beachcombing in the west. Smooth-surfaced, buoyant and toughly enduring, Caribbean drift seeds sifted as rarities into Ireland's coastal culture. The largest, *Entada gigas*, with a skin like fine Moroccan leather, is also the commonest and is recorded in Irish names: *sliogán boilead* on the Dingle peninsula, *sceartains* on Tory Island. It was first noted on Irish beaches in 1696 and was sometimes tested on teething babies or fashioned into key rings and snuff boxes.

The bean drops from the metre-long pods of woody vines, a source noted by physician and herbalist Sir Hans Sloane on travels to the West Indian islands in the 1700s.

A mortuary of fascinating flotsam

But its modern natural history, together with a guide to other drift seeds reaching Ireland, had to wait for a twentieth-century Irish botanist, E. Charles Nelson, then on the staff of the National Botanical Gardens in County Dublin.

Dr Nelson's speciality is garden heathers, but his *Sea Beans and Nickar Nuts*, published by the Botanical Society of Britain and Ireland, remains the most popular of his forty books. It includes, I am proud to say, a drawing of the large, fibrous husk that crowns my bean bowl – the only specimen of the tropical box fruit *Barringtonia asiatica* ever gathered from a European shore. I had found it on a winter tideline of Mayo's Inishkeas.

A few miles north of Thallabawn strand is the long, sandy beach of Carrowniskey. Keen surfers arrive when big breakers build up in autumn, and a high shingle ridge makes a grand-stand for watching horse and pony races in July. As I perched on its slope on quiet winter days, the colours and patterns in the big, ocean-rounded cobbles came to trigger my still-tenuous grasp of Mayo's rocky basement. They heaped limestone on sandstone and granite on schist, with the odd black and polished egg of dolerite, or a pillow of conglomerate welding pebbles of pink and green. In days before I knew to leave the landscape alone, I took some home for garden sculpture.

The great mineral mix of Carrowniskey was woven in Ireland's long journey from the other end of the Earth and in multiple upheavals, sunderings and spells beneath the sea. It traces a history of almost 2,000 million years that makes Mayo a focus of student geologists. In their favourite pub in Louisburgh, a map of county rocks hung behind well-fingered glass on the wall.

At the far north-west corner of the county, the dark and banded gneiss of Annagh Head is some of the oldest rock in Ireland. Further south along the upland rim of the Wild Atlantic Way, the Nephin Mountains and those of Achill and Croagh Patrick are wrapped around cores of quartzite, the stuff of posh kitchen countertops. Earth's pressures hardened this from sandstone, common in the skin of the old volcano stubs at Mayo's south-western corner, where I live.

The volcanoes of the Ordovician era, explosive and long-lived, reared up in two halves of Ireland, small fragments of the planet once widely separated by an ocean, the Iapetus, and welded together when the ocean was swallowed, 500 million years ago, in a continental collision. This hoisted a basin of sediments to surface today's high plateaux of the Sheeffry and Partry hills, lined up behind Mweelrea at the north of Killary Harbour.

Mweelrea's wind-carved summit

At 814 metres, Mweelrea, behind me, is Connacht's highest peak. Its summit was left bare above glaciers in the last ice age, making it a nunatak, a lovely Inuit word for such protrusion. On the top today, frost-shattered slabs of stone still clatter under one's boots. Two great waves of ice, one covering Ireland completely, served to scour and shape the Mayo landscape. They ground across the limestone that stretched in from the midlands, framing today the great Mayo trout lakes of Mask, Carra and Conn. Dramatically carving the mountains north of Killary Harbour, glaciers helped to scoop out the long fiord itself and left Doo Lough Pass to brood over corries and moraines. East of Clew Bay, as final thaws took hold, the rush of water in tunnels beneath the ice moulded till into the whale-shapes of drumlins, little hillocks that became islands in the glacial estuary of the bay. A commanding view of them is among the rewards of climbing Croagh Patrick, as thousands of people, mostly Catholic pilgrims, have done for so many years.

In the 1980s, the mountain's sacred significance was challenged by a proposal to mine gold from beneath its western slopes. It was one of several such projects prompted by the discovery of the mineral, glinting grain by grain in quartzite veins of south-west Mayo. Among early prospectors, one had parked at our gate on a snowy day in March to set off up the hillside, metal dish under his arm, to sample gravel in our hill stream. I joined him for a token swirl of grit in the icy water. It seemed I might, with enough time, extract enough gold from the stream to make one little bracelet charm.

The prospector of streams was followed in due course by a mining company's chief exploration geologist, a cheerful, bearded young man with a deep wind tan, keen to enlist my interest in his local explorations. He took me for a hike across the floor of Doo Lough Pass, where tough quartzite ridges rose in waist-high 'creggans' from the bog and marched west towards the mountain. What he'd found, said his company, was 'a westerly plunging, tightly folded volcanic horizon which holds extensive gold mineralisation up to a depth of 160 metres'. The 'horizon' pierced the mountain ridge to its seaward side with average assay of about six grammes to the tonne, or as much as a good pinch of salt.

This was enough, however, to warrant hauling a drill to the hill above Kinnadoohy, its jib sticking up from the skyline as I sat at my desk. The tip of a finger would blot it out, but when the wind went north or dropped, the whine of the drill took over my mind and could drive me, with my word processor, to the other side of the house.

Ravens over Doo Lough

The quartzite belonged to Mweelrea's Ordovician rocks, stretching down to a seashore promontory and surfacing again offshore in Inishturk. The consequent designs of a second mining company, however, were foiled by the islanders' unanimous decision not to let its gear land: they would blockade the harbour. The Croagh Patrick project was similarly doomed by public dissent, and the one for Mweelrea, a valued landscape after all, was overtaken by creation of the Wild Atlantic Way. Inishturk stands at the centre of my workroom view, its hilly profile lighting up in a first glow from the sunrise.

In Mayo, more island adventures began in the company of David Cabot, a devoted field ornithologist and friend who lives between the lakes behind the shore. With David at the outboard tiller, a rubber dinghy took us out on his regular winter visits to the Inishkeas, to assess their flocks of barnacle geese, and to less accessible islands in hope of netting and recording their rarities.

The Bills Rocks, for example, were a possible breeding haunt of Leach's petrel, a scarce little bird of the open sea that sometimes kept company with storm petrels, the chirruping familiars of stone walls and burrows of many deserted western isles. From the coast, the isolated Bills

make sharp little marks on the horizon. Close up, their dark
and precipitous walls echo with surging sea sounds. On a first
reconnaissance, the swell was too great for landing on seaweedy
rock slabs canted at forty-five degrees. On another day we
succeeded, hauling up the dinghy, engine and camping gear to
the foot of a cliff we could climb. We camped overnight, high
among the sea pinks, a mist net stretched out in the dark. Its soft
mesh pockets were to offer storm petrels for ringing by David,

Inishturk view

who has a licence for such delicate work. And there was, indeed, just one of the starling-sized Leach's, its white rump shining in the light of my torch.

Later came Duvillaun, out in the sound between Inishkea South and Achill Island. A cross-carved pillar speaks of early monks, and a long-empty bothy of pre-Famine occupation. Its gable walls were densely felted with long fronds of *Ramalina*, a lovely grey-green lichen that thrives in the pure ocean wind. From another, tense landing on wave-washed rocks we pitched camp beside the bothy, to film grey seals suckling their pups at their autumn nursery in a cove below the cliffs. This gave us good footage for David's Bolex 16mm camera, but also touched a flaw in my pretensions as director.

We were set up on a crag overlooking a mother and pup in a long, sandy crevice between high rocks. The tide was rising, the white-furred pup still suckling. As waves surged in, it was eventually torn away and dragged back and forth in the foam, the mother curling after it. Seal pups must choose between suckling for more strength and learning to swim, but I found its struggles agonising. There came a critical point at which it was dragged away to drown and I called upon David to stop filming. He properly ignored me, recording the close to a perfectly natural drama.

*White-furred seal pup
stranded at dawn*

As an American/Irish graduate of Trinity College Dublin, David had discovered the wintering flocks of barnacle geese on the Inishkeas and saw their regular migration to the islands as a long-term population study. It was to become his obsession for more than sixty years, and for a number of them I joined him on mid-winter visits to the geese.

On a grey day in January, as so many of them were, the long Mullet peninsula has the bleakly improvised look of a settlement at the edge of Arctic tundra. The treeless land is puddled and bone-bare, the houses clustered on sufferance from the wind. At my first embarkation, the strand where we readied the dinghy for Duvillaun Mór had been scoured, only days before, by the thirty-foot waves of a storm. It was such a storm, in 1927, that overtook the island fishermen in

Barnacle goose family on their cliff top nesting site in Ørsted Dal, NE Greenland.

their currachs and drowned ten of them, and a relentless run
of gales that led to the final evacuation in 1934. The western
rim of the south island is heaped with a jumbled storm
beach of huge, dark blocks of stone. A narrow channel that
separates north from south was finally carved through by
storms, and those of today surge across a low neck of land
with a threat to slice the Inishkeas into an archipelago.

In all this, the geese curve their necks to peck grass at a
furious rate, producing a new dropping every four minutes.
These scattered green cheroots are still nutritious and
hoovered up by the cattle occasionally brought out to
graze the islands.

Barnacle geese, sleekly brocaded in silvery white and black,
are strangely aloof and inexpressive, some two thousand of
them seeming mere clones of one. But they are curiously
loyal to the parts of the island they first land on, the same
birds coming back to the same fields year after year. To
bring scattered flocks together for David's telescope and
his routine census of their leg-rings, I set off round the
shoreline, putting up geese in eruptions of muscular wings
and puppy-like cries of alarm. I found a flock at the very
edge of the towering western cliffs and paused there in awe
of the storm-riven landscape. On a close-cropped meadow

of the northern island, a flotsam of wind-blown trawler floats, brightly coloured, were scattered like billiard balls waiting to be potted into rabbit holes. On each island, a selvedge of deserted houses lines the eastern shore. When I first came to them in the 1980s, most were roofless and rabbits had burrowed beneath the hearths. The one we lodged in, however, had a stout front door and a sturdy, concrete roof that rang like a gong in the worst gusts of a storm (one of many that held us for nine days).

We slept beneath a ceiling of long spars and driftwood gathered from the shore. But the door looked out to the remains of the island's industrial history. Among them were the rusted vestiges of a boiler that had drawn the oil from whales killed and hauled ashore in the early 1900s for flensing into chunks of blubber.

Centuries before this noisome episode, another nature-based trade earned the Inishkeas an international reputation and a place on early maritime maps. A French archaeologist, Françoise Henry, exploring the coast below Bailey Mór, the great mound on the northern island, found traces of an intensive industry in a dye extracted from sea snails. It made the famous Tyrian purple, a badge of imperial fashion in the Roman Mediterranean and named after Tyre in Lebanon.

Stormy sea and threatening clouds at Thallabawn

The shellfish that yielded it was Ireland's common and native dog whelk, *Nucella lapillus*, a thick-shelled whelk not much bigger than a winkle and of the same family as those of the eastern Mediterranean. Its tough armour allows it to roll about in stormy seas as it seeks to latch on to young mussels and barnacles to drill through the shell into their flesh. The animal's purpurin gland yields a defensive poison that turns purple only on exposure to air. How its use was discovered, developed and promoted from this remote western island remains a mystery, but it may speak for the early trade and cultural contacts of western coastal Europe.

The whalehunters

The great painter of Mayo landscape, Paul Henry, visiting
Inishkea South in 1907, was shocked by the squalor of the
whaling station at Rusheen, where blood ran into the sea.
The smell 'was appalling,' he wrote, 'and so bad was it that
it was a couple of months before I got it out of my clothes.'

> There was a tremendous amount of offal which was
> being thrown to the pigs of which there were great
> numbers on the island, the most enormous pigs I
> ever saw. They were all over the shore, dragging at the
> huge lumps of flesh with grunts and cries and I was
> warned not to go near them they were so savage.

The ventures in whaling, based first on Inishkea South and
then on the mainland at Blacksod, were driven by Norwegian
entrepreneurs, supplying their own steamers and crews.
The boats were armed with explosive harpoons fired from
cannons in the prow.

In his unique chronicle of the industry, *Irish Whales and
Whaling* (1981), university zoologist James Fairley accepted
the surprise of such a history:

It is enough to say that nearly 700 of the great
whales were slain in commercial operations off
Co Mayo between 1908 and 1914, that the first ever
recorded use of a harpoon gun was in Donegal Bay,
and that its inventor contrived to kill fin whales
with his weapon in the mid-eighteenth century.

In the 'best' season at Rusheen, more than one hundred
whales were killed, all within sixty miles of the island. Blue,
sperm, sei, right and humpback whales were quarry along
with the fin whales – an early measure of the migrants using
the continental shelf west of Ireland. In 1991, with David
Cabot as an environmental adviser, Taoiseach Charles
Haughey introduced protection for cetaceans in Irish
waters. My own knowledge of whales and dolphins, as I
began a morning patrol of the long strand at Thallabawn,
was scanty at the least. Greeted by bottlenose dolphins,
swerving along the crests of waves, I wrote of them as
joyous 'porpoises' with a quote from *Moby-Dick*. And
nothing could forgive my careless reference, in an early
column for the *Irish Times*, to finding a dead and stranded
'killer whale'. What could have been a discovery of some
significance, given the current chemical threats to orcas,
drew James Fairley to drive for two hours from Galway.
His inspection of a bulbous-headed, long-finned pilot
whale, a common stranding along the Irish shoreline,

was brief and choleric: the professor did not suffer fools at all and protested to the editor. His trust was slow to earn, but a few years later we knelt together on the strand, in a sand-blasting wind, at the five-metre corpse of one of the rarest beaked whales known to science.

The first specimen to be described and named was washed ashore in North Carolina in 1912. It was found by a biologist, Frederick William True, a mammal curator with the Smithsonian Institution, and his excitement was expressed in the animal's scientific name, *Mesoplodon mirus*,

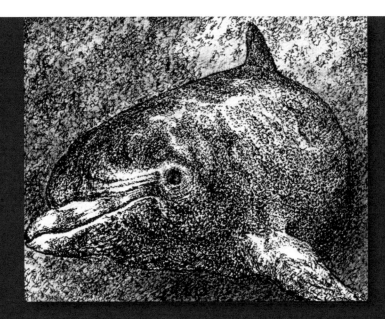

Bottlenose dolphin

or True's 'wonderful' beaked whale. Mine seemed to be only the seventh or eighth found anywhere at all, which felt wonderful indeed.

The family of slim, beaked whales are deep-diving animals thought to feed mainly on squid, but their teeth seem remarkably few for the job. Indeed, True's boasts only one short pair, jutting at the end of its lower jaw, and their precise angle and oval shape are key to its identity.

The professor had come equipped with a little red hatchet, and it was the toothed tip of the jaw, carried off in his rucksack, that was to clinch the whale's distinction. If that weren't wonderful enough, and most remarkably, a second True's turned up on the strand a few month later, its presence quickly passed on by neighbours. Some smelly work with a hacksaw sent the key portion of jaw, with twin tusks, to James Fairley in Galway. His identification was then endorsed by a cetacean expert in the British Museum in London.

This all took some time. The whale, meanwhile, was sinking slowly into the sand, and each spring tide foamed a little further into the holes pecked by great black-backed gulls. The British Museum, the

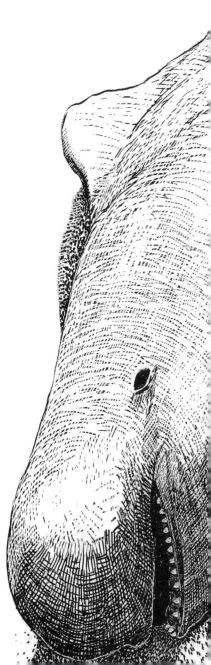

Ulster Museum and our own Natural History Museum were agreed that it would be a fine thing to recover the whale's skeleton for future reference and display, but the logistics and finance presented problems. Eventually, it was the Ulster Museum that arrived, its pristine rented van carefully lined with plastic. It was driven by Terry Bruton, a museum technician of some accomplishment, whether in the slicing of rocks, the curing of skins or the stripping of animals down to their bones.

A burly, ebullient man from east Belfast, he had started out in life as a sheet metal worker and was now a committed naturalist, inspecting with enthusiasm the small skulls, shells and bones that littered our window-sills. Down at the strand, all that could now be seen of the whale was a slight hump in the sand with a gory hole pecked in it and the cup of the whale's eye floating on the sand like a water lily. A semi-circle of watchers stood at a judicious distance, well upwind, and glad of a rising gale. As Terry took the lead with a spade, I asked how he would cope with the whale's effluvium, now rising around us in sickening waves. 'Same as always,' he replied 'olfactory fatigue.' A long slope of meadows separated the strand from the van, and I prevailed on a young neighbour with a tractor and transport box to ferry the chunks of whale as Terry, now in a thigh-deep pit, severed them from the bones.

His big butcher's knives were constantly blunted by the sand, and he paused to sharpen them on a steel as if carving the Sunday roast. When one of the knives slipped and fell, perhaps to be buried, a neighbour thoughtfully retrieved it for him, offering it on the blade of a long-handled shovel.

Terry Bruton was later made curator of mammals at the Ulster Museum. Subsequent years saw a sadly significant increase in stranding of beaked whales, including fourteen True's, on our western coasts from County Donegal to Cork. The toll of Cuvier's beaked whales reached five in one day in 2018, as recorded by the Irish Whale and Dolphin Group. Diving deeply to five hundred metres for food, beaked whales seem fatally susceptible to submarine sonar waves transmitted in naval exercises.

Loggerhead and leatherback

My early years of beachcombing found other, more portable, corpses that led to more books and reports on my natural history shelves and to a singular trophy for my workroom wall. 'Trophy' seems to fit the appearance, like a large, tribal war shield, of a dark and curving turtle carapace almost a metre long. A rim of rough spikes creates its warlike aura. This big loggerhead turtle, *Caretta caretta*, came ashore so convincingly whole that preserving some spirit of it seemed obligatory. I brought a wheelbarrow down to the strand and hoisted the animal into it, then trundled it back up the hill, its big head lolling over the front, hoping not to meet any neighbours. I buried it in an empty potato lazy bed, trusting the fauna of the soil to set about recycling the softer parts. I had, however, reckoned without the attentions of our little black dog, who visited the ridge from time to time to chew off the rim of the carapace, leaving points of bone to protrude.

  The world's largest hard-shelled turtle, the loggerhead is mature at almost a metre long. Its east Atlantic casualties succumb to the chill of winter seas and storms, sometimes arriving at an Irish beach in January, alive but comatose with cold shock. An aquarium may attempt a very slow revival.

Loggerhead turtle in wheelbarrow

Leatherback with jellyfish

In great contrast of size were my couple of finds, on a winter shore, of the rare Kemp's ridley turtle, an exquisitely moulded creature the size and shape of a dinner plate. At the time of my finds, in the 1980s, their numbers had dwindled to some two hundred, nesting on one or two beaches in the Gulf of Mexico. Today, with protection, their population has climbed back to some nine thousand, but no more than ten have been recorded in Ireland. I immured one of my little ridleys in a box of sand, and later kept its delicate netsuke of a skull in a plastic chocolate box. Left too long on a sunny windowsill, it fell apart into confetti. The other ridley is safely pickled in the 'dead zoo' of the Natural History Museum in Dublin.

A hugely bigger turtle, the leatherback, *Dermochelys coriacea*, was for years a victim of entanglement in drift nets and the ropes of lobster pots and hauled out, dying or dead, for public inspection. This is how I saw my first specimen, displayed on a little fishing quay on the south of Achill Island, the salty tears from its jellyfish diet still oozing from its eyes. By that time, the 1980s, such actions were becoming rarer, as knowledge of the leatherback and its ocean lifestyle was absorbed by Irish fishermen.

This was partly due to the personal crusade of an amateur naturalist, Gabriel King, who had seen a leatherback entangled in gear off Quilty, County Clare, and persuaded the fishermen to secure its release. He discovered in the process a complete lack of awareness of the turtle's protection under the Irish Wildlife Act of 1976. This set him off on his bicycle on a mission to all of the Republic's fishing ports. A slightly built, mildly spoken young man, he braved quayside bars from Donegal to Kilmore Quay in County Wexford, gathering fishermen's encounters with leatherbacks and engaging their support in his quest for their conservation.

As late as the 1960s, the world's biggest turtle had been treated as a rarity in northern European waters, vagrant from tropical warmth. But underneath this reptile's smooth, rubbery shell, ridged from front to back, is insulating blubber that retains the heat generated by the use of its great flippers. Maintaining an inner body temperature, in cold water, almost eight degrees warmer than its surroundings has enabled it to travel north habitually, pursuing the abundance of jellyfish around these islands and becoming a species protected by Europe's conservation laws.

Basking shark – an endangered species

In 2022, another very big Atlantic migrant was admitted to Irish protection, after a history of slaughter centred on Achill Island. It was by chance, early in my Irish explorations, that my bicycle took me to Keem Bay and a grassy perch above the sea. As I gazed down at men in three currachs, something very big, dark and vigorous was twisting in between. Their arms lifted to strike downwards with harpoons. The big shadow stilled among the meshes, and the great fish was towed to a corner of the cove. It was one of the last basking sharks, as it happened, to die in this obsolescent industry.

Its history went back at least two hundred years to the flicker of oil lamps in cabin chimneys and the glow of street lights in eighteenth-century Irish towns. Even after paraffin fed the lamps, basking shark oil was the richest source of squalene, an extra-fine industrial lubricant and cosmetic moisturiser for the human skin.

As the world's second biggest fish, next to the whale shark, *Cetorhinus maximus* can grow to eleven metres and weigh up to four tonnes. Its exceptionally large and buoyant liver can weigh half a tonne and yield up to 400 gallons of oil. Huge and harmless, sieving plankton from the waves and lacking any predator but people, the shark takes up to twenty years to reach maturity and perhaps a few more gestating a handful of two-metre pups. With sustained mortality from hunting, the population falls.

By 1962, the Achill fishery for basking sharks had virtually collapsed after a decade of peak catches. In the early 1950s, Irish fisheries averaged 1,475 a year, but I was watching the death of one of perhaps fifty drawn in late spring to the plankton-rich swells around the Achill headland.

Protected now from hunting, the shark is still considered endangered in the north-east Atlantic, but its behaviour can suggest a puzzling exuberance. During watches off Malin Head, County Donegal, in 2015, a 'hot spot' for basking shark gatherings, a research team videoed the giant fish bursting from the sea in brief and ponderous flights of breaching – no fewer than six hundred such acts over ninety hours of observation. The effort is comparable to the leaping of South Africa's great white sharks and even more costly in energy, but possibly part of the same show-off mating behaviour.

Some of my own awesome experiences of nature have had to do with very small things. I'll start with one that came as I stood on an island of sphagnum moss in the middle of a little peaty loch on a hillside on Clare Island, the largest of Mayo's offshore terrains. Beside me was Pete Coxon, a palaeobotanist from Trinity College Dublin with a gifted mission in probing Ireland's past. Beyond him were the lichened slabs of a court tomb built 5,000 years ago. But under our feet were some 10,000 years of peat and lake mud. They filled a basin once occupied by a block of ice as the glaciers pushed west out of Clew Bay. How deep the hollow went we didn't know.

Pete Coxon's special skill in palaeobotany is interpreting the mix of plant pollens and bark fragments brought up from the depths of the modern landscape. They arrive in a plug of ancient mud, about as thick as one's thumb, retrieved from the end of a very long tube. We joined in pushing down successive sections of the tube as far as it would go.

Even with the grip of four fists, heaving up some five metres of tube became progressively more difficult: the past was letting up its secrets with a stiff and sucking reluctance. But in the final core was a thrilling surprise. The bronzy mud, with its flecks of birch bark and fragments of twig, had a band of charcoal that marked a period of forest burning some 7,500 years ago. And below it – at, say, 8,000 years or earlier – was embedded a whole and flawless hazel nut. It came from a time of slow climate change. The glaciers of the last ice age had finally melted and a rising sea level had cut off Clare Island from the mainland. The first grasses and docks had shed their pollen, then the hardy juniper, slender hazel and birch, their spring catkins shaking out masses of pollen. Some of it was washed into the little lake at Lecarrow, followed by some of the hazel nuts. Ireland's first humans, the Mesolithic hunter-gatherers, may even have picked some on this hillside.

Once extracted, the nut's exposure to oxygen began to darken its golden brown shell, and within an hour it was almost black. Coxon kept it 'to show to Frank'. This had to be Professor Frank Mitchell, the much-admired guru of Trinity's landscape analysis. On a treasured visit to me at Thallabawn, we had walked the hillside together and he had made me aware of the likely Neolithic origins of some sunken stone walls and a grassy trough that could have been dug for a *fulacht*, the improvised cooking pot of early hunting parties. My favourite image of Frank Mitchell, culled from his writings, was of him kneeling on a patch of sandy silt at Achill's Ashleam Bay, picking out some five thousand fossilised willow leaves from 11,000 years ago to make up a sample big enough for the carbon dating of the time.

In the title of his splendidly discursive book *The Way That I Followed*, Frank Mitchell made a bow to the classic of Ireland's exploration of landscape and the natural world, Robert Lloyd Praeger's *The Way That I Went*. The two men were contemporaries in academic natural history and equally devoted

to sharing their enthusiasm more widely. Praeger's giant accomplishment was the exhaustive scientific survey of Clare Island that he mounted, with the Royal Irish Academy, at the start of the twentieth century. Repeated by the Academy in the early 2000s, few places on Earth and none elsewhere in Ireland have yielded such a concentrated inventory of knowledge about a piece of the natural world. Praeger had a driving inspiration in recruiting more than one hundred scientists to the venture. He was fascinated by Charles Darwin's theories of evolution, especially of species

Praeger and fellow fieldworkers on Clare Island during the Clare Island Survey, 1909-1911

Photograph courtesy of Royal Irish Academy

on islands. Even though Clare Island had so recently been part of the mainland and was still within a blackbird's flight of it, Praeger hoped it might still show some evidence of separate adaptation.

In the event, this was rare. But, as ecologist John Feehan wrote in *Clare Island*, an overview of the surveys: 'It can be hard to believe that Clare Island is home to more than a thousand different animals.' They were found and studied, from near-invisible mites on the seashore to lichened boulders on the summit of Knockmore, and then extended, in the second survey, to the surrounding subsea world of kelp forests. Between the two surveys there had been great change in the island's human world and use of the land. The second team of scientists found a bare island overgrazed by sheep, its heather cover lost to wildlife. Arable land was grassed over, and the domestic economy now related to the supermarket. But the island has attracted new settlers, and plans for its future include eager concern with restoration of the natural world.

Along with sheer awe at the hazel nut retrieved from times long past and suddenly resting on my palm, I'd place the delight of finding my first *Janthina*, the lovely violet sea snail, freshly delivered on a gentle summer surf to the pristine outer sands of the Mullet peninsula. I'd first read of its curious story in a book on the sea by Rachel Carson, the American biologist globally remembered for early warnings on the dire potential of the pesticide DDT. In one effect, this made the eggs of falcons too fragile to hatch their young. And, as it happened, the fragility of *Janthina*'s shell had made it a rarity on the rocky shores of Maine that were Carson's favourite beach-combing territory.

She longed to have one for her marine collection and once tried to buy the only specimen in a shell shop in North Carolina. Rebuffed, she waited on luck, and

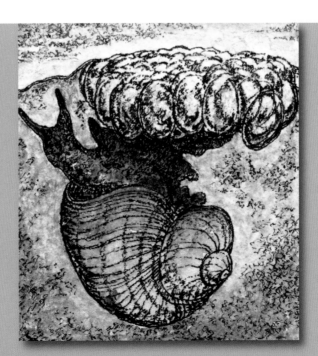

The floating violet sea snail, Janthina

'later I found an empty shell, light as thistledown, resting in a depression in the coral rock of Key Largo, where some gentle tide had laid it.' Reading this, I knew her joy, having come upon two of these beautiful, translucent shells, resting within a pace of each other on the tideline. It was a privilege all of a piece with *Janthina*'s random lifestyle, since this mollusc travels the surface of the ocean hanging upside down (as we would see it) from a silvery raft made by trapping the wind in bubbles of the snail's own mucus.

It lives on the chance of colliding with, and eating, a little blue jellyfish called *Velella*, or by-the-wind sailor, sometimes cast up by the million on Ireland's Atlantic shores. These, too, are ocean drifters, propelled by a little rainbow-coloured sail set diagonally on the float to catch the wind. The odds against snail and jellyfish colliding on the open ocean seem enormous, yet they do this with sufficient frequency to be bonded as predator and prey. When by-the-wind sailors drift ashore, *Janthina* occasionally arrives with them, but snail and jellyfish first meet, far out on the ocean, by bobbing blindly against each other, like toy boats on a park pond.

Velella's blue jelly underparts and tentacles dry out rapidly on the beach, leaving only the rainbowed, oval disc embedded in its surface and its small, transparent, triangular sail, like cellophane, set upright and diagonally across it. These are more durable structures, like bits of plastic, and often what the holiday beachcomber stoops for and puzzles over. Part of the puzzle is that, on some floats, the sail is set NW–SE; on others, NE–SW. In the same wind, one animal will sail leftwards, the other rightwards, either veering as much as sixty degrees away from the wind's direction.

This engineering scatters the species widely, being mixed as larvae (or so it is hypothesised) in the middle of the ocean. In the northern Atlantic, where winds twist eastwards in rotation of the Earth's atmosphere – the Coriolis effect – it is most often the left-sailing *Velella* that end up on our beaches. In July 1992, they came ashore almost simultaneously along a four-hundred-kilometre stretch, from Cork to Mayo. Tens of thousands choked rock pools in Connemara, and more edged the tide in continuous ribbons. At Thallabawn I gathered hundreds, some the size of my palm, others just a few centimetres across. Of my handfuls of discs, 228 were left-sailers and 42 were right-sailers, which seemed to match the general design of Coriolis.

Banded grove snails

Behind the dunes

The natural world of the seashore has prompted most of my narrative: it is where so much has happened. But to climb through the marram grass of the dunes behind the strand is to follow a link in an ecosystem, between land and sea, that unites the lives of some of their animals.

When I came to it first, half a century ago, the flat, grassy plain behind the dunes, shaved by wind and hammered flat by rain, seemed a strange, idyllic lawn with a few white rocks for sitting on. What it meant to the natural world took time to learn.

I joined the locals in calling it the *duach*, respecting the echo of lost Irish, but to ecologists and geographers it's *machair*, a word from Scots Gaelic. The landform was classified first on the isles of the Outer Hebrides, then mapped along the windiest edge of Ireland from Donegal to Connemara.

It is floored and renewed with sand blown in from the strand, much of it made from fragments of seashells – 'the toe and fingernail parings of the sea' in Michael Longley's indelible image. Arriving ashore, the fragmented calcium of marine molluscs – mussel, periwinkle, cockle and the rest – along with that of crab shells and sea urchins becomes material for building the shells of land molluscs, the multicoloured snails that throng the dunes and *machair*.

A local example of global recycling, this delighted me. Many of the snails are the large, brown, 'ordinary' species of urban back gardens. On a moist morning in late spring, they seek each other out for a passionate entwining, and I have found it difficult, walking in the dunes, not to crunch them under my boots. In winter, they line up close together in the crannies of rocks and on the lee side of weathered shore fence posts, where the gales sandblast their shells to delicate shades of blue.

Another set of snails are much smaller and slimmer and prettily banded with yellow and brown. These are the grove snails *Cepaea*, common in the Pyrenees and believed by some researchers to have arrived in Ireland with Mesolithic seafarers – perhaps even as pocket snacks for the voyage. The wetter parts of the machair host rare snails of Arctic provenance, small as a match-head and needing an eyepiece to examine them, as visiting malacologists regularly do. And botanists on their knees have also needed to magnify a rare plant, *Petalophyllum ralfsii*, of which the machair is a refuge. This liverwort then appears as an exquisite, bright miniature of a lettuce. Michael Longley made his usual magic of it in a generous little poem after I shared with him my wish to have my ashes scattered on the strand. The final verse runs:

Let us choose for the wreath a flower so small

Even you haven't spotted on the dune-slack

Between Claggan and Lackakeely its rosette –

Petalwort, snail snack, angel's nosegay.

Michael's 'soul-landscape' has been centred on Carrigskeewaun, 'rock of the wall ferns', Thallabawn's adjoining townland on the shore. Here, for some fifty years, with wife Edna, their children and now grandchildren, he has driven from Belfast to spend weeks in David Cabot's cottage, perched between machair and lake at the foot of Mweelrea Mountain. In his poem 'The Wren', he describes Carrigskeewaun as 'a townland whooper swans / From the tundra remember, and the Saharan / Wheatear.' It has been the birthplace of Ireland's greatest modern nature poetry, taking wing across the world. To be with Michael in the landscape has been to know nuances of feeling quite beyond casual experience. Once, trudging over the bog, high on the slope under Mweelrea, we came to a stream braided into separate strands among the mosses. He suddenly hushed me, still as a fox. He could hear two separate chuckles of water, and, finding the point at which their music balanced in the ear, invited me into it. To share the landscape with him was to discover many such magical spaces in the mind.

Skylark above the duach

Compared with the watery weave of Carrigskeewaun, no wild fragment of Ireland has been more closely parsed and adored. Longley has recalled its changing embrace: how, at first, the hugeness of its space and horizons drew the eye, then the intricate middle distance of little fields and dry-stone walls. 'Finally, you end up on your hands and knees, taking it all in.' Love of wildflowers has been a thing we share, but the genes that prompt it may have differed between us. My enjoyment has been cued rather simply to aesthetics, to colour, form and fragrance. In a memory from infancy, tiny blossoms crept across the gravel of the backyard, a dustbin alley in Brighton walled with Sussex flints. Pimpernel and toadflax made a fingertip bouquet of lilac and vermillion, offered to my mother frying chips in the kitchen for the street cafe above.

Early in the 1940s, evacuated to a country aunt, I rushed to sow seeds in her garden: bright marigolds and scented mignonette. Back home, I plundered luscious roses from abandoned wartime homes, but also the little yellow poppies of a town dump up the valley. With war ended, and barbed wire uncoiled from the shore, I climbed a chalk cliff to pick the clove-scented stocks that had rooted in its crevices. Given such a disposition, the midlife move to an acre of thistles and grasses, with a sheltered hollow and a stream, should have prompted grand floral designs – and did indeed from time to time, as visiting gardeners pressed suggestions (tree ferns for the hollow?).

  Too late now: it would have needed another life, with less attention to growing food and perhaps a lot more money. Some gestures remain among the tangle of trees and enveloping fuchsia thickets and the hillside's infiltrating grasses: the sprawl of cranesbill geranium, invasive tussocks of lady's mantle, a hillock of climbing roses, a clump of miscanthus beside the boggy pond: survivors all, even among the obdurate brambles of old age.

Michael Longley's love of flowers must be no less for their beauty and even more, as a poet, for the powerful music of their names, but as a vigorous classicist and once a teacher, he takes his botany seriously, seeking out the experts as guides. One, Charles Nelson (already introduced about sea beans) had written a brilliant companion to the flowers of the Burren, and led Longley through that limestone wilderness. Another was the Belfast botanical artist Raymond Piper, a friend whose eccentricities often frustrated the care of his superb gallery of Ireland's orchids, painted over forty years.

In the Burren, kneeling with Piper, Longley inspected the dense-flowered orchid, a distinctively Irish rarity. At Carrigskeewaun he found stands of another, the lovely Irish lady's tresses, wound with tiny white blossoms. But perhaps his most memorable wildflowers were those he listed in a poem, simply and at length, as a life-affirming gesture of dismay at the murder of 'the ice-cream man on the Lisburn Road.' Line by line, they were the twenty-two flowers he had seen in one day in the Burren: nothing very rare, but a life-affirming roster beginning with thyme and ending with bog pimpernel, all defiant of such reasonless death.

Invocation of otters

Paw-prints on the tide-washed sand … not the mincing,
hurried, straight-line trot of the fox at break of day, or the
random scatter of a lolloping dog, but crisp insignia as
elegant as sculpture-marks in stone: five oval toes, then
five again in the otter's unhurried passage from wave to
land. Our adored mammal commutes to the lakes to wash
its warming underfur of salt, or to the dunes to chew on
a fish among the marram. Once, walking the tideline,
I found myself witness to a remarkable little drama.

Pursuit by a raven

An otter emerged from the surf with a flatfish in its mouth and carried it up to the ridge of the dunes. As it settled down to eat, a raven appeared, hovering close and greedily over the otter and its feast. I stayed frozen and amazed as the big bird clawed at the fish. After some minutes of harassment, the otter gave up and slid back down the dune, bearing what was left of its dinner back to the sea.

Michael Longley co-starred in another encounter. For a sequence in a documentary film about him, made with David Cabot, I wanted to show him paddling in the surf while his voiceover offered his poem 'Sea Shanty'. It was a November afternoon with dark clouds on the horizon, but he bravely paddled forth, wellies dangling from one hand, shins turning blue. The take went well. As we joined him for close-ups (beard trembling in the wind), we were watched by a distant neighbour, shovelling shell-sand into his trailer. It was from that direction the otters came: two big cubs in tandem, galloping in and out of the foam. The camera, still on its tripod, had film; the light was perfect. The otters held to their line, then swerved gently around us and melted into the waves. We giggled and shouted. 'An invocation!' cried Michael.

In my personal experience of the natural world, little could have seemed more exotic and exciting than to join in an Arctic expedition. That one became two and even more adventurous sprang from David Cabot's commitment to his long study of Inishkeas barnacle geese. He needed to include observation of the breeding of the geese on the cliffs of north-east Greenland.

His first expedition, in June and July of 1984, took three ornithologists and me to Ørsted Dal, a tundra valley halfway up Greenland's eastern coast. We were landed finally by helicopter, but study of the nesting geese in eparate colonies took thirty days of walking and climbing (in my foolish, Mayo wellington boots) and many hours on clifftops noting on cards the endless, possibly significant, shifts in the birds' behaviour. David Cabot filmed, for the first time, little goslings jumping off the high cliffs to find food. Some bounced off rocks, others were snapped up by Arctic foxes prowling the scree below.

In one marathon operation, pursued far into the amber-lit night, some six hundred moulting and flightless geese were rounded up into a netted pen for ringing and weighing. Just three were birds Cabot had ringed on the Inishkeas; many of the rest later migrated to Scotland.

The second, three-month expedition, beginning at the end of May in 1987, took David and me, with Irish botanist Roger Goodwillie, to the wilderness of Germania Land, some hundreds of kilometres north of the last High Arctic weather station. It was one of the least explored regions on Earth. Greenland's mobile, military Sirius Patrol had reported seeing barnacle geese in the valley of Klaegbugt at 77°40′N 20°51′W. This was enough for Cabot to gamble that the birds might include more of those he had ringed on the Inishkeas.

Germania Land, before the thaw

In May in the late 1980s, the impact of climate change on the Arctic was already under way, but scarcely evident around us and far from our minds. The Twin Otter chartered from Iceland soon flew above fractured floes, and while its first landing on the fiord of our valley brought a frightening plunge of a ski through the ice, a second circuit touched down securely, leaving us a longer haul of gear to the shore and a few watchful glances to the fiord's icy distance for the approach of polar bears.

On the night we set up camp, the loudest sounds in the valley were the wailing and eerie mating calls of great northern divers – 'loons' as Americans call them – echoing from a small lake below the cliffs. But even as we pitched our tents, an arrow-head of barnacle geese flew in above our heads – a first reassurance of the journey's success. These birds – some thirty pairs for study – proved to be one of seven cliff colonies, the most northerly barnacles ever known. As dutiful scientists, Cabot and Roger Goodwillie spent 150 hours perched among high and unstable boulder scree for continuous watching of the nests. From his pre-carious perch, Cabot filmed the regular but extraordinary leap of chicks from the nest ledge to the rocky floor of the valley, where Arctic foxes waited to snatch them up. Then came the rounding up, from the valley's small lakes, of the

There were butterflies – a few on warm days – and a busy long-haired bumblebee with a dissembling buzz that was not a helicopter coming after all.

moulting and flightless parent geese. More than one hundred were ringed, most to be sighted again as migrants to the Scottish island of Islay.

The expedition aims for Klaegbugt were broadly ecological, from reporting on its plants, lichens, mosses and fungi to dating the first sighting of mosquitoes (22 June). As Goodwillie assessed the valley's vegetation, he used skills that, a decade before, he had applied to the whole landscape of County Mayo. Among the 110 plants and grasses he recorded at Klaegbugt were the arresting successions of flowers, all speeding up their cells to use the brief season of sunlight. The rising warmth of climate change is now drawing up the height of prostrate shrubs such as willow and many of the grasses, but the sequence of flowering of different plants is slow to change. It begins with the amethyst gleam of purple saxifrage, its flowers brilliant at the edge of melting snow. Later come the silken white sweeps of mountain avens, golden stamens at each heart, cushions spreading on stolons rather than by seed just as in the Burren. There were butterflies – a few on warm days – and a busy long-haired bumblebee with a dissembling buzz that was not a helicopter coming after all.

For that long-ago summer, at least, the valley still held all its wildlife. A lone wolf with yellow eyes came to visit as we

sat eating supper, attracted, perhaps, by the scent of curry.
It stood beside us as we froze in wonder, until Cabot's reach
for the film camera sent it away. It ran across the valley to
harass a small herd of musk oxen who at once formed a circle
around their young, confronting the wolf with sharp and
lowered horns.

Dark lumps of musk ox wool swung from any sharp rock of
the tundra, as the animals rubbed off the thick winter coat that
so inflates their size. The many hares, on the other hand, had
stayed as white as snow, their turn of speed outrunning any
predator. They grazed on flowering yellow poppies and their
leverets peeped in to my tent.

What, then, of bears? In my fifty-fourth year I was physically
quite timid and quickly anxious, but refused to obsess about
them. In preparation for the worst scenario, our trio had been
taken to the Wicklows to practise shooting with a heavy game
rifle. My success in hitting and pulverising a moderately
distant (and unmoving) concrete block offered some grim
hope for my chances. On the low approach flight to the fiord,
I had noted the size of the bear tracks on a snowy ridge below.
In practice, neither of the expedition's ursine episodes was
fraught. In the first, the three of us were perched on a cliff
above the fiord when a mother bear appeared on the ice below,
closely trailed by a fully grown cub we assumed to be her

daughter. The mother was huge-shouldered and beautiful, the sun gleaming in every white hair of her coat. She seemed also determined to shake off her grown cub to its own devices and repeatedly turned and hunted her off to find and lie beside her own seal hole.

A night or two later, as we settled in our tents, a thud of falling boxes arose from our food stores, stacked just metres away. I reached for the flares I hoped never to use, but Cabot seized his camera and emerged. His film followed the bear's swift retreat to the fiord: perhaps, we chose to think, the daughter bear, foiled on an early forage of her own.

In the myriad branches of evolution, where did polar bears come from? Little is known of their history, but in 2011 a research team led by Dr Ceiridwen Edwards, an archaeogeneticist at Trinity College Dublin, suggested an origin in matings with brown bears wandering out from refuges in a glaciated Ireland. Hybridisation in this rapid, climate-driven dispersal left 'a strong genetic imprint' that, the team concluded, had helped to shape the polar bear's matrilineal descent.

The brown bears lived on in Ireland. Huge numbers of their bones, mixed up with those of woolly mammoths, were excavated around 1900 from limestone caves in County Clare. Among them was one with deep notches that could have been made by a Stone Age butcher using a long blade of flint.

Their dramatic significance had to wait on a routine reanalysis by Dr Ruth Carden in 2006 and a radiocarbon dating of their DNA. The result was to change the proven existence of humans in Ireland – the bone was notched 12,000 years ago, a whole 2,500 years earlier than previous archaeology had suggested. This had been the lifetime's work of Professor Peter Woodman, who, in the 1970s, discovered the traces of a Mesolithic settlement at Mount Sandel, overlooking the River Bann in County Derry. This was dated to 9,000 years ago, but the butchered bear bone pushed back Ireland's first human hunters from the Mesolithic into the Palaeolithic and the final ebb and flow of the Ice Age. Woodman accepted that Sandel was 'the earliest known site and there may be something marginally earlier', but he thought there was 'little chance of discovering a significant, missing, yet-to-be-discovered Palaeolithic'.

On an island so changed by ice and the loss of offshore landscape in the post-glacial rise of the ocean, only the jumbled bones of the caves remained as clues to the animals surviving the last throes of cold and into the earliest years of human settlement. Just when they existed had to wait on today's refinements of radiocarbon dating. The genetic lines of DNA are also called upon in attempts to trace the origins of the mammals in Ireland today. Just two suggest survival through the last ice age: the stoat and the Irish hare.

The stoat's wavy hemline

What makes a stoat Irish?

In my first encounter with an Irish stoat I showed a shameful lack of empathy with the natural world. It was in the winter of my early, 'sabbatical' year in Connemara, when I was matching meagre savings to my food supply and welcomed anything free.

Returning up a bog road with a bag of mussels gathered from a local estuary, I was halted by piercing animal screams from the bordering moorland. A stoat tumbled out on to the road at my feet and backed off from the big, plump rabbit it had killed with a bite to the base of the skull. The potential gift proved irresistible. The stoat circled around me, eyeing the rabbit now swinging from my hand, then followed as I set off up the road. Nearing my rented cottage I caught a glimpse of my follower on top of a stone wall and hurried indoors with my hijacked prey. As Giraldus Cambrensis wrote in the twelfth century, the stoat can be 'vindictive and relentless in its wrath'.

I remembered this sad affair decades later, on a similar encounter on a stony shore, and made a point of backing off from the stoat and its feast. In one hard winter, a stoat from our field bank arrived at the kitchen windowsill to feed on crumbs put out for the birds, having scrambled up a whale skull that leaned against the wall. In this unexpected close-up through the window, I could see what makes the

Irish stoat distinctive: the wavy lower edge to its chestnut cloak, unlike the straight trim of its British cousins.

Small, outward differences also mark the Irish hare, with shorter ears than the brown hare of Britain. It is a unique sub-species of the Arctic mountain hare that has adapted in Ireland to grazing down to sea level, as in our coastal fields at Thallabawn. It is the only other native mammal to have survived the Ice Age, with cave fossils dating back 28,000 years. But while the stoat could have survived in Ireland by eating lemmings under the snow, just as in Greenland, the hare is thought to have colonised Ireland during the Ice Age from dry land to the south-west, now below sea level that rose with the melting of glaciers.

The extent of Ireland's maximum coverage with ice was not appreciated until a few years ago. It had been judged mainly from geological impacts on the land, but new seabed research has changed the map dramatically. Abundant seabed scrapes from icebergs and ridges of gravel from land rocks have shown that the glaciers spread out from the west of Ireland right across the continental shelf, fed by fast-flowing ice streams, and that ice was flowing down the Irish Sea until 16,000 years ago.

How this related to Ireland's post-glacial colonisation by its 'native' mammals is still under debate. Some, like the hares, could have waited out the Ice Age in refuges on seabed left dry to the south of Ireland. Others, such as badgers, were brought from Britain by early settlers for resources of food or fur. For Ireland's tiniest mammal, the pygmy shrew, the story is more complicated. Its genes could be traced to Andorra, north of Spain, and several of Ireland's plants and invertebrates are thought to have come in boats from Iberia. But pygmy shrews need to eat almost constantly to survive: how many beetles would they find on a long trip from Spain? More likely, it's thought, they came in hay for livestock, brought from Britain.

In our preparations for moving west, and with 'self-sufficiency' in mind, we commissioned a currach from a craftsman from Inishturk. He built one as if for the island, with a comfortable inner lining of lath and a strong, square transom for an outboard engine. This was obviously not a cockleshell craft to be borne to the waves on the shoulders of one middle-aged townee and his wife. The currach lay alone above the dunes, its bottom up for me to tar once a year, until its sale to a wiser man.

Ireland's tiniest mammal, the pygmy shrew

The sea, meanwhile, in the strangest of demonstrations, offered samples of fish we might have caught. On the night of a fierce storm, it drowned scores of them and cast them up along the tideline. They were fresh, gleaming and eminently edible, with the help of cat and dog. I strung twine through the gills of whiting, silver hake, pollack and ling and stuffed the big game pockets of my Barbour jacket with multicoloured wrasse, gurnard and black, tadpole-shaped lesser forkbeard (named from a poster in our kitchen). I left behind the remains of a large and hideous angler fish with a toothy grin like a Cheshire cat and a huge conger eel I didn't fancy for the freezer.

All were fish of a rocky bottom or offshore reefs and shared gill coverings and pelvic fins bent the wrong way, as if overtaken by a sudden, explosive surge of water. Hundreds more fish of similar kinds littered the shores of south-western bays, prompting one marine biologist to suggest they had been choked by sand stirred up by a month of heavy swells, an exceptional but natural phenomenon.

In with the spillet

We were never to see it again as we embarked upon another way of taking fish from the sea. An island friend knew how to make a traditional spillet. Ours was a long line coiled from a bucket, branching fifty baited hooks and anchored to the seabed at each end. At one low tide, with night to come, I waded in to set anchor and buoys beyond interference from hovering gulls. At dawn's low tide, crucially timed whatever the weather or sea-state, I waded in to haul anchors and the catch of fish or seaweed.

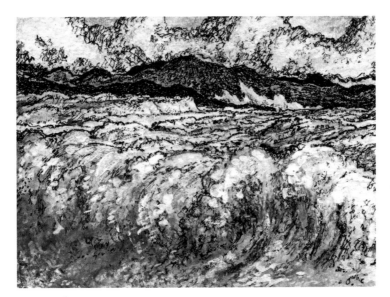

Wild waves at Thallabawn

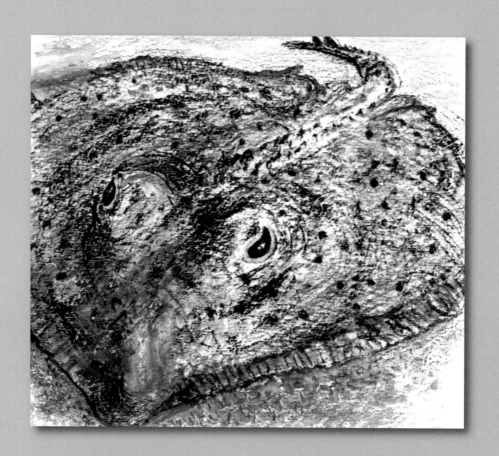

Thornback ray on sandy seabed

Our optimal quarry was the common thornback ray, armoured with barbs on its upper side. On its underside is a deceptively gentle-lipped mouth with a bite – I discovered – like the grip of a teething baby. It's close to the skate in the elasmobranch family, a fish now rare in the west and quite fished out from the Irish Sea. The thornback became a staple food of the workers in Dublin's Ringsend, a village derided as 'pissy' from the pervasive smell of ammonia. This came from ray wings pinned out to dry in the narrow streets. The fish's ammonia does, indeed, take a little time to leave, but the wings are then nourishing, sweet and delicious.

Our other fishing enterprise was catching eels in the wetlands behind the duach. For this we had come equipped with a fyke net, to be staked out in deepish water overnight. It steered the eels into either of two long cones of net, like windsocks, to trap them at their ends.

I didn't catch many and was finally dismayed at the death of a young otter that had wriggled too far into the net. Nor had I been happy with the surgery on the sand to take just the wings from rays sometimes half a metre across. As I hauled the line in, they had skimmed the last waves as if flying. And then, stabbed dead and butchered, they were left to the gulls like dismembered violins.

Among the heather

New lives for old goats

It is an autumn night in the shed, with the stream gurgling by, and I am kneeling on the straw with the bucket, milking Nancy, while her daughter shares the shadows with the cat. The flashlamp lights a glint in Nancy's eye as I practise the two-tone squeeze that brings milk jetting from her teats. I tell myself we feel, perhaps, a bit bonded in some ancient, hippy sort of way...

Among the happy memories of our ventures in 'alternative' living, this is certainly one of the best. It came about through Ethna's capacity for turning milk into cheese, a skill she had acquired to pass on to farmers' wives in north Mayo as some small contribution to saving the west. It needed a set of aluminium moulds, finely fabricated by local Travellers (once 'tinkers'), and Ethna had treasured them, together with their press, when the wives' lack of interest finally prevailed.

We enjoyed all the cheese but not the problems of confining the goats' own appetites among our vegetable beds. The intimate experience of them, however, left me with a special respect for the long and fascinating story of Mayo's native, landrace mammal, the Old Irish Goat.

Nancy was a Saanen, short-haired, pure white and of Anglo-Swiss breeding for milk yield and amiability. Along with the Toggenburgs, the Saanen has been a mainstay of Ireland's substantial goat farming for extra-digestible milk and delectable cheeses. But such refined and companionable animals are different creatures from the wild, shaggy goats of Mulranny at the northern corner of Clew Bay. Their small, wiry body is sheathed in a thick and floppy hearthrug of a fleece in a dozen different patterns of grey and umber. The male, with sweeping, show-off horns, and a wispy Confucian beard, is some two hands shorter than a big Saanen billy and quite outclassed in authority by the oldest nanny, leading the flock.

I glimpsed them first among bushes of Mediterranean heather on a hillside beyond Mulranny. This was also where, in the 1930s, they were encountered by the great Robert Lloyd Praeger. As he wrote in *The Way That I Went*: 'They fit in so naturally among heather and gnarled rock, and mount a miniature Matterhorn with such a regal, king-of-the-castle air!' Until this century, the animals went their way largely unremarked, except on their winter incursions into the village gardens of Mulranny. But in the past decade, recognition of their venerable bloodlines has swept them into attention as a rare and authentic Irish breed, surviving a peasant past when the goat was 'the poor man's cow'.

Their new significance began with the dedicated interest of Dr Raymond Werner, a UK historian. More than half a century of research into old races of European and British goats left him convinced that an Atlantic 'cold-weather' goat evolved even earlier than the Neolithic origins of farming and was domesticated by pastoral, Mesolithic nomads.

Many centuries later, and based in the west of Ireland, they formed the travelling dairy herds taken to Britain on tours needing hundreds of miles of walking. DNA samples from goat heads mounted on Mulranny walls and from museums showed a close relationship to those of extinct populations in the Inner Hebrides dating from the 1800s. This has supported Werner's scenario of 'goat men of Armagh' collecting their herds from Connacht for travelling around Scotland. His 'cold-weather' genotype for the Old Irish Goat includes some unexpected insulation: 'Small, cobby, round barrel, long-faced, small pricked ears, harsh outer coat, abundant cashmere undercoat.'

When their omnivorous browsing can be controlled and directed, the goats may well have a future in conservation grazing. This has been tested on both sides of the island. On Dublin's Hill of Howth, where wildfires follow the spread of whins, or gorse, a herd of trained Old Irish Goats has been recruited to feed on the shrub, discouraged from invading neighbouring gardens by alarms from digital collars.

In west Mayo the problem is gunnera, the huge 'Chilean rhubarb', introduced as a garden ornamental on Achill in the nineteenth century. By 2018 it was raising its enormous leaves and seed heads at more than a thousand sites on Achill, forming dense thickets on agricultural land and crowding the island's bog roads.

With support from the local authority and Atlantic Technological University, a herd from the Old Irish Goat Society was set to work at Currane in the autumn of 2022, browsing on the gunnera with relish. Their final destruction of its thousands of seeds remained to be seen.

Just beyond Croagh Patrick, on its eastern footslopes, Brackloon Woods share in the moist coastal air and its oaks offer hanging gardens of polypody ferns, lichens and mosses. It has also become the state's model for restoring native woodland. Brackloon's oaks are themselves not especially old – perhaps two hundred years at most – but they all grew naturally, springing up from acorns or sprouting from the stumps of still older felled trees. These, in turn, had grown naturally, in continuity from the native forest that greeted Lord Altamont when he came to his Westport estate in 1650. The modern oaks survived a mass felling of the forest's trees in the 1960s and their replacement with conifers.

Today, with the conifers gone, remaining stands of oak, and others mixed with ash and willow, cover almost a quarter of the wood as remnants of the natural forest climax of the west. Beside them grow planted birch trees. With sheep kept out and rhododendron removed, oak seedlings have been able to grow, along with the mosses, liverworts and wildflowers of an open woodland floor. Fallen oaks are left where they lie, for insects, fungi and soil bacteria of deadwood to recycle into fresh organic nutrients.

The restoration of Brackloon and its value as a field laboratory for woodland science had to wait on Coillte's removal of the conifers. That came after Roger Goodwillie's pioneering survey of Mayo in the 1970s. His long list of potential conservation sites did include, however, other oakwood fragments, such as those at Pontoon and Barnarinnia, facing total eclipse from sheep grazing and state conifer forestry.

His survey was basically botanical, but it did embrace bird life, geology and zoology in choosing habitats at risk. He was specially concerned to protect those on the Mayo coast 'before the full impact of European buyers' prompted to seek safe havens from the political storms of the day. Old Head was among the state nature reserves created in 1984.

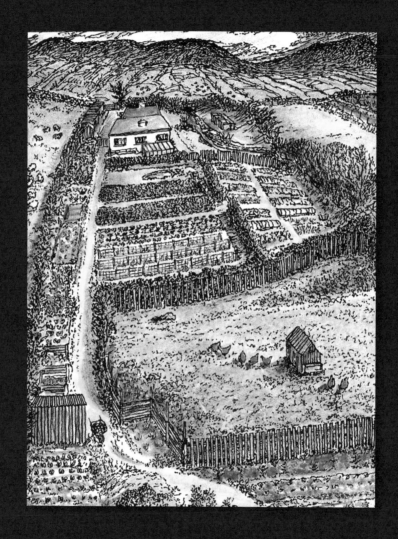

Our acre in production

A tangle of trees

Our own little woodland now covers most of the Irish acre that came with our cottage. Its trees are a random tangle of species given rooting space between vegetable beds, now long abandoned. One or two trees arrived on their own – a crack willow and a hawthorn – while some, like the oaks and ash, were intermittent gifts; a lime was in memory of a friend. I must have bought the birches and rowans, and I let the horse chestnut grow from buried conkers. We stole a volunteer whip of beech from somebody's forest and it now peers over everything, even the sycamore that tried to seed a forest of its own. Together, their dense medley of branches have cushioned the worst of storms from the sea.

Beech peers over everything

In the many years that it nourished us, I gave thanks many times for the kindly fortuities of the acre itself. For the fact, first of all, that it tilted to the south and received the sun all day. For the fact that it sloped at all, draining surplus rain away and letting me walk the land, or dig it, at almost any time of year. And that it sloped the right way from the house, inviting a loaded wheelbarrow downhill.

Then, above all, that its soil was good for growing things besides trees: a sweet, deep, sandy loam ground fine by ice and time. How easily, caring only for location and holiday views, we might have settled for a patch of acid, rushy swamp or a rockery of cutaway bog. Each spring, the soil felt better in my hand, its mineral grains webbed with humus and root fibre from all the laborious tons of compost and old dung from the farm down the hill.

Every forkful held a few earthworms, if not a whole squirming company, a gardener's key allies in the natural world. As the soil's engineers, their tunnelling creates a network of tubes that drain away excess water and bring air to the roots of plants. They pull down fragments of compost or fallen leaves, sensibly seizing the pointed end first, as Charles Darwin observed (he offered a variety of leaf shapes cut from paper). There was an early time when I let hens or a robin dart in to seize a worm, but I soon learned more

Earthworm, the gardeners' ally

respect for the invertebrate life of the soil, its mites, ants, beetles, bristletails, bacteria, all working away for the health of what Americans dare to call 'dirt'. One gramme of grassland soil can hold more than ten thousand different bacterial and fungal organisms, all a part of the ecosystem that stores carbon in the skin of the Earth. But how do I get on with the bigger creatures of soils and shadows and under stones, those so often disdained as 'creepy crawlies'?

Once, in a dank and ferny corner of the greenhouse, I came upon a beetle burying a wren. It was not so extraordinary that the little bird should have died (unable, perhaps, to remember the hole it came in by and eventually running out of spiders and moths), but the chance of watching such a burial by a sexton beetle – the name arrived from somewhere – was a one-off occasion.

The insect was black-bodied, glossy, with bright orange, bushy antennae. It was working alone, whereas the burying beetles more often celebrated on Google are a woodland kind with bright orange bands on their bodies, seen working in marital pairs, and thus, perhaps, more likely to catch the human eye. This one, *Nicrophorus humator*, had yet to attract a mate, but meanwhile laboured on, using its pointy, jagged forelegs to drag crumbs of soil backwards from beneath the wren's feathers.

It was going to be a long job, but it didn't mind me watching. Insects never do: it's part of their otherness, like the disturbing animation that moves their robotic little legs. As the wren sank crumb by crumb into the soil, I went indoors to read up on burying beetles, the genus *Nicrophorus*. I did know their purpose, to provide a hidden larder for their grubs, and thus, in the process, recycle the wren's constituents, but not that they would spray its skin with anti-bacterial enzymes to slow the bird's decay underground. These, apparently, are rich in lysozymes, also secreted in mammalian breast milk and human tears, such is the ramifying biochemistry of life. Finding out about insects, so rich in the unexpected, has definitely improved some of my entomophobia. A wincing distaste for earwigs, for example, has become somewhat more benign from knowing that they make fantastic mothers. What more knowledge cannot assuage, it seems, is my lingering arachnophobia.

A mini-trauma of my own childhood, at a therapeutic 'open-air' school in Surrey, was the communal panic of nuns on discovering a big, black specimen of *Tegenaria domestica*, the house spider, in one of the dormitory washbasins: they ran to pour whisky on it, their own black fabric fluttering and rustling in alarm. Is this why, while I'm able to regard most spiders

Devil's coach horse beetle, dearg–a–daol

equably enough outdoors, a dark and twisted tomato calyx left casually on a kitchen countertop can still arouse a split- second shudder? I don't have to feel too badly. The great evolutionary biologist and student of insect societies, E. O. Wilson, was once offered a huge, hairy, leg-waving spider by children in New Guinea and later wrote that it made him feel 'panicky and sick'. So much – to be quite unfair – for his famous theory of 'biophilia', the innate affinity of humans for the natural world.

How far are we born scared of its less familiar creatures as a cautionary, evolutionary reflex against harm or disease, and how much is culturally conditioned? An American entomologist, Jeffrey Lockwood, once traumatised by envelopment in a sudden swarm of grasshoppers, is persuaded that young women are especially prone to irrational fear of insects and snakes and so pass this on, as mothers, to the great bulk of humankind.

I still seem to blame black insects for looking sinister – nothing could be blacker than the *dearg-a-daol*, lifting its little tail in threat, like a scorpion. Chitin, the thin, hard shell, the exoskeleton, that encases most insects and crustaceans can, I suppose, be any colour, and the violet sheen of some beetles is quite attractive. But black does accentuate the alien articulation of insect joints and legs and gives disquieting pause about what, exactly, makes them move.

Chitin wraps the bodies of hoverflies, too, and even the veins in their wings. These tiny, flying pollinators, no bigger than my thumbnail, are banded in bright colours and among my favourite insects. Summer is confirmed for me when I'm stopped in my tracks by a glint in the air a step or two ahead of me: a spark of pure sunlight with just a hint of colour, a tiny whirr of wings that makes a space-shift sideways, or up or down in a sudden, quantum bilocation. Having shown off for a while, it is suddenly not there any more.

There should be a special name for what the hoverfly does so instantly and geometrically. I thought I'd found it in a research paper from Brighton, my youthful bailiwick. 'Saccades' sounded likely, but no, those are the insect's sharp, sideways movements of the eyes, fixating its targets, like a taoiseach checking round the cabinet table. On the other hand, such fixation helps the insect zero in on its targets whatever the air turbulence, like the 'steering by gazing' mechanism of some aerial robots. What's being tracked are other hoverflies, often with reproduction in mind. 'The male rapes flies of either sex,' say the researchers, 'indicating that successful copulation involves more trial and error than recognition.' The often jewel-bright livery of Ireland's 180 species of syrphids (as hoverflies are known scientifically) puts them among the 700 or so European species compiled on the remarkable database – called, neatly, Syrph the Net – compiled over twenty years by Dr Martin Speight, long the leading entomologist of the National Parks and Wildlife Service.

Selection of hoverflies

Its big value lies in predicting which hoverflies to look for in a particular habitat, such as woodland or wet grassland, and for their larvae in microhabitats within them, such as ponds or stands of particular plants. Some hoverflies are anthropophobic, living aloofly in natural broadleaf forests rather than conifer plantations, cultivated farmland and hedgerows or anywhere else that man hath wrought. Fortunately, many more are anthropophilic, or farmer-friendly. The adult females need flower pollen as protein for their eggs, and their larvae eat hundreds of aphids, both to the great benefit of many human crops.

The one I most often see, standing still just to watch it, is ringed distinctively in yellow and black, which has made 'the marmalade hoverfly' an easy name for *Episyrphus balteatus*, common in Irish gardens and cereal crops by late summer. It does overwinter here but mainly arrives in migrant swarms from Europe. The first record of this came in 1995, when two biologists in a boat off Courtmacsherry Bay in County Cork saw skeins of hoverflies heading for the coast in company with clouds of red admirals. The flies were so numerous that dead ones were forming drift-lines on the sea.

Aphids, too, are among the teeming numbers of insects now known to populate the sky, sometimes passing overhead in billions per month at heights of up to a kilometre. They are a staple food of swifts, helping to sustain their life in the air and feed the chicks in nests in urban eaves.

The study of insect life in the sky has grown with the use of radar. In its early technology, baffling shadows on the screen had to gain recognition as flocks of migrating birds. But refinements in vertical radar and analysis have now distinguished the varying flights of insects, often making equally purposeful journeys. In the fast-developing science of radar aeroecology, the mass of invisible insects once regarded as 'aerial plankton' has been resolving into identifiable species, many far from passive in taking off and landing and choosing a direction in the wind.

The regular migrations of insects with larger bodies, such as day-flying butterflies and dragonflies and night-flying moths, have been intensely studied, but the flight behaviour of migrant hoverflies, more vital to control of crop pests, is now yielding to radar research. Using fast-moving airstreams at more than 150 metres above the ground, their return migration in autumn may head into unfavourable winds, but uses the sun as compass.

An English ornithologist, David Lack, once climbed to a high summit pass in the Pyrenees to check a theory that

Europe's migrating small birds might find some mountains too hard to cross. The theory was wrong. David with his wife, Elizabeth, counted hundreds of finches, linnets and other small birds skimming the pass southwards back to Spain. With them came butterflies – clouded yellows and red admirals – and dragonflies at the rate of several thousand an hour. At first they didn't notice the hoverflies, tiny black-and-yellow ones, pressing on at ankle height into the wind. What caught David's eye at last was 'a shimmer of iridescent light, due to the reflection of the autumn sun on myriad tiny wings'. Their species was *Episyrphus balteatus*.

The insects of the sky include millions of the tiny spiders that fly on gossamer threads to unguessable destinations. I have sometimes felt my cheek stroked by invisible threads while walking down the garden path on a still, balmy autumn day. Even a sometime arachnophobe like me can't mind the caress of an aerial voyager a couple of millimetres long, whose landing – on one's left hand, is it? – might bring some money or luck.

One autumn I crouched on a hillock over at the far lake to enjoy the whooper swans, newly arrived for winter from Iceland and dipping their necks deep for waterweed. Beyond them was the cliff, brilliantly rimmed by the sun at midday, so that, backlit against its darkness, their beaks came up dripping diamonds. Then I noticed, high above the water, hundreds of

The whooper swans' lake

shining gossamer threads, hanging almost vertically in the still air sheltered by the cliff. It was my first revelation of the secret life in the wind.

In northern Europe it's mostly the *Linyphiidae* family, the little 'money spiders', that go ballooning like this, along with young spiderlings of the *Lycosidae*, or 'wolf' family, which don't sound as friendly. They perch on tip-toe – eight tip-toes, I suppose – on a high point, perhaps on a fence post, to catch the wind.

Then they squeeze out silk threads, typically half a dozen, from the spinnerets in their abdomen. Entomologists have differed on whether the spider lets the wind keep tugging the threads out, or if it anchors them first and pays them out in stages. When the threads are long enough for lift-off, perhaps a metre or more, up the spider goes.

Charles Darwin, watching this in South America, thought the thread 'glittering in the sunshine, might be compared to diverging rays of light; they were not, however, straight, but in undulations like films of silk blown by the wind.' Aboard the Beagle, he found thousands of small, red spiders in the rigging when the ship was still a hundred kilometres off the coast of Argentina.

Almost entire populations of spiders, young and adult, can be prompted to leave home, given the right conditions and pressed by food shortage or overcrowding. In one remarkable experiment, at a sewage works in Birmingham in 1980, dispersal was closely measured for a week after two filter beds were deliberately dried up. The spiders, bereft of flies, climbed bicycle spokes planted in the gravel and took off in their millions.

The balloonists can rise to great heights. An antique biplane in America sampled them at up to 4,500 metres, its struts sometimes webbed with gossamer on landing.

Descending and discarded strands, intercepted by trees, can bring spiders as food for birds.

The fallen flights of threads, catching beads of dew or mist, can set grassland gleaming. A Dublin architect, walking in the Phoenix Park one December morning, reported 'an infinity of strands of silk stretched upon the grass as far as the eye could see. Close by, they shimmered in the sunlight like a moonlit sea...'

On our living-room wall, above the woodstove, hangs a circular bronze shield marvellously embossed and entwined with symbols of sport, music, arts and crafts. This was the Tóstal shield, from a 1950s festival of Irish culture prompted by the post-war Festival of Britain. Among its national competitions was one for wrought-iron work; another, for trout fly-fishing, was won by my late father-in-law on the choppy waters of Lough Mask.

For Seamus MacManus, leisure revolved around his boat on the Mayo shore of the lake and the mayfly season, his set of rods and his wallet of flies: dapping mayfly and golden olive much the best. He took me out once, hopeful of a keen companion, but my ineptitude at casting proved discouraging. Mayo's big limestone trout lakes are not at all what they were. Once they had flourishing populations of Arctic char, the herring-like fish that most likely was the first into

Ireland's post-glacial rivers. Living in deeper, colder water with plenty of oxygen and great purity, they have been succumbing to modern conditions and climate change, and whole populations have gone extinct.

I should like to have been there when Seamus caught his one and only pike, played in to his boat, I suspect, on light fly-fishing tackle when the big fish gulped a trout on the line. Taken home to his kitchen table, it took a visiting daughter aback, the sudden shock of its alligator jaw and fixed stare remembered for life.

The pike was long regarded as an alien predator, introduced in the 1600s and awarded the Irish name *gaill iasc*, or 'foreign fish'. But then it was found that an even older name, *liús*, like the old 'luce' of England, chimes with the pike's Latin surname, '*lucius*'.

Today's genetic analysis, by a team at University College Dublin and Inland Fisheries Ireland (IFI), saw Ireland's pike arriving in two separate waves, the first from Europe around 8,000 years ago in freshwater flows from melting ice, the second as introductions from Britain in the Middle Ages, mainly into southern rivers.

The same close research brought surprises on the pike's choice of prey. Distinctively shaped for fast take-off in ambushing fish, it is highly opportunist in its choice of food.

Pike or gaill iasc, *'foreign fish', only 8,000 years in Irish waters*

Roach and perch dominate its fish prey, but invertebrates such as *Asellus*, an aquatic woodlouse, account for more than half the diet in nearly all Irish waters. And while pike can grow to giants (one was caught in the Erne at 46 lb), comparatively few reach the size for tackling trout. This has not spared it, however, from persecution as a supposedly alien villain. It was often blamed for declines in trout stocks at a time when many other causes – sewage and farming pollution, overfishing, arterial drainage, competition from introduced roach – were also taking their toll. Beginning in the early 1950s, some 36,000 pike a year were culled or transferred, notably from the great trout lakes of the west. Removal of pike from Lough Mask, by electrofishing and netting, is continuing IFI policy.

North of Mask and connected by a river, Lough Carra was the largest and best of the marl lakes left on Ireland's limestone after the Ice Age – perhaps, indeed, the best of its kind left in Europe. It is so charged with calcium that its bottom of white marl gives a special colour to the water – 'a wonderful, pale pellucid green' as described by Robert Lloyd Praeger a century ago – but tending now to murky shades of jade as summer wears on. From a crystal-clear oligotrophic (or nutrient-poor) lake, it is now mesotrophic and perhaps on its way to eutrophic, a word all too familiar in decline of water quality.

In today's watchful world of ecology, mayflies are a key signal of the health – or sickness – of lake waters. Their larvae, or nymphs, live on the bottom for up to two years, growing and moulting a score of times before surfacing as bright-winged flies and taking to the air. Carra once had phenomenal hatches of mayfly – so prolific that millions of dead insects washed up along the shore. Today, their population has fallen and the lake's exceptional angling for big, silvery trout, adapted to gin-clear water (the record weight was almost six kilos) has been thrown into doubt.

Carra is fed from small rivers in a farmed drumlin landscape, and the run-off of slurry and fertiliser has clouded the water with summer plankton. Waterweeds crowd in on a rare bacterial crust of its boulders, called Krustenstein, and algae turn the marl of the lakebed from snowy white to green. The lake has been well studied. A book by ecologists and anglers Chris and Lynda Huxley documented research over decades and has helped prompt local commitment to environmental action, not least to keep Carra's water fit to drink. But while the lake is well garlanded in natural protection orders and a marvellous wreath of lakeshore orchids, it awaits the proper management of an ecological treasure.

Bog cotton blowing in the wind.

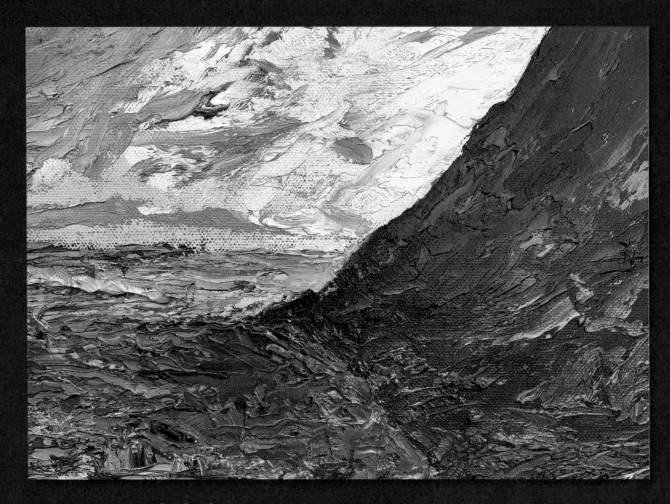

Doo Lough (detail)

Epilogue

My attraction to a 'wild' corner of the rocky Mayo coast has roots in a Romantic and aesthetic movement born in the eighteenth century. Before that, a 'beautiful' landscape was one made by people – cornfields and orchards – and much of the mountainous and boggy west would have been seen as nature at its most uncontrolled and threatening.

There was no science of ecology to inspire the English Romantic movement of philosophers, painters and poets, but their rich intuitions helped people to value a relationship with nature. They helped to shape a landscape, and a free and popular affection for it, that were denied such fruitful cultivation in Ireland. Natural history, as a hobby and an enthusiasm, belonged largely to an occupying, colonial class, along with much ordinary, communal enjoyment of the living countryside. Quite where Irish rural life and sensibility got torn away from the older Gaelic expressions of oneness with the natural world is hard to measure. The desolation of the Famine showed nature at its least obliging. The utilities of living and the absorptions of religion proposed other things to think about. 'Natural life,' wrote Patrick Kavanagh, 'lived naturally as it is in the countryside, has in it none of that progress which is the base of happiness... Rural life is all background.'

This cultural lack of feeling for the natural world created problems for policy-makers charged with the novel politics of conservation. They craved facts and figures and common measures of human benefit, crystallised today in such economic terms as 'ecosystem services' and 'natural capital'. The pollinating work of bumblebees had to be given a cash value.

Roger Goodwillie's survey of 'areas of scientific interest' in Mayo in 1979 was like those prepared for every county in the Republic by An Foras Forbartha, Ireland's first conservation agency. The pigeon-hole term of 'scientific interest' split the conservation of nature from ordinary, popular concern and, later, helped to justify following EU nature directives as impositions from Brussels.

In the half century since these early moves in conservation, a profound development for many ecologists and environmentalists has been the Gaia hypothesis conceived by the English inventor and scientist James Lovelock. His theory of the planet's life, now widely accepted, treats Earth as a single, self-regulating, living system. Species work together in ecosystems, and global warming arrives as an ultimate demonstration that 'everything connects to everything else'. This has been at the core of the great awakening to the natural world in the twenty-first century,

Golden eagle, Mweelrea

hammered home by endless exposure of its damage and decline. Fear for nature has been welded to fear for the human race. In the blunders of the Anthropocene, the era of human dominance, we may not be 'threatening the planet' – it will carry on without us – but we have affected Earth's systems in ways that make our own survival uncomfortable and insecure.

The notion of humankind as a transient species, despite our exceptional gifts of intelligence, raises the idea that other, existing species and their habitats have an intrinsic claim or 'right' to exist, other than simply being part of what Gaia contrives. Respect for such a 'right' even entered the urgings of Ireland's Citizens' Assembly report on biodiversity. In philosophical terms this is difficult, since 'rights' can scarcely exist outside of human values and structures.

Intuitive support for the idea can come from rejecting certain biblical teachings about human mastery and exploitation of nature, now often amended by urgings of 'responsibility' and 'stewardship'. Farmers have traditionally been seen as guardians of the countryside and its natural world. But their use of land has been shaped by government research, advisory services and farming media, all heavily influenced by a technical culture of intensive production and ever-more-elaborate machines. What most farmers know

Hillside farm

of nature, in the ecological sense, is more likely to come from watching wildlife films on television than from much attention to the birds and insects around them.

There's irony to the thought that the peak of Ireland's lowland biodiversity was probably at the time of small, mixed farms with a social rationale not far above subsistence and self-sufficiency. It was low-income farming without tractors

Doo Lough (detail)

Corncrake calling

or artificial fertilisers and managed for family life with the minimum of bought-in food. In one study of a Galway townland as run in the 1940s, the farmers kept Shorthorn and Hereford cattle, Galway ewes, Clydesdale and Irish draught horses, Large White and Landrace pigs, four or five breeds of hens, and assorted ducks, geese and turkeys. The crops included oats, wheat and barley, potatoes, mangolds and turnips, and sugar beet for a factory.

Each group of crops, each kind of livestock, plus the stone walls and hedges of small, sheltering fields, created particular niches and habitats for insects, birds and small mammals. The loss of mixed farming has cost us the corn bunting, brought the corncrake and grey partridge close to extinction and made the yellowhammer a rarity across most of the island. It has also made much of the countryside a less interesting and desirable place to live.

As I enter my nineties, much of our acre is so full of mossy trees that sea and mountain are screened by millions of leaves. Too many are borne on the briars that arch between them. The old hawthorns on the western bank have lost their balance in the wind and are bowed down into shelter and warmth and heavy with blossom and berries. This involuntary 'rewilding' has changed my natural world, making it forbiddingly tangled and layered. There used to be flowers and tortoiseshell butterflies; now, speckled woods dart and fight among the shadows. How soon, I wonder, will local wildlife find this a desirable place to live? As one particular, will it ever again play out the sad feud of predatory badger and hedgehog?

The acre as we came to it had not been grazed for years. Its vegetation was still rank with thistles and scutch grass. Kneeling at an early vegetable bed, I heard sharp snuffling from nearby cover at the foot of a bank and paused while the hedgehog – it had to be – moved on. Later I met my first in prickly person, ambling down the boreen on a sunny evening. When the boreen was surfaced, and traffic grew, the flattened hides of road casualties were, for a time, far from rare.

And then, for drama, came the night a hedgehog raided the eggs of a nest our maverick ducks had secreted in brambles on the bank of the stream. An anguished quacking brought us out with a torch at midnight. Hunched up in its glare, the hedgehog continued to feed among the shells. I used tongs to extract it from the briars and put it in a coop overnight. By morning it had duly found a hole for escape.

What, then, of any feud with badgers?

Badger at moonlight

Across the fence, among dense willows, years of floods in the hill stream had helped build a sandy mound that badgers had tunnelled in an elaborate sett. Its occupancy since was a mystery, like the badger holes still piercing dunes at the shore. For a run of years, around February, a badger came under the fence to gather fresh bedding for its underground chamber. Out to the rain gauge each morning, I would find big tufts of dried grass and twigs it had collected along the hedge-bottoms, then dropped on the path as too much to carry (once, it was daffodil leaves). I did meet a small, bedraggled badger returning to the fence one morning, unburdened with bedding; it paused for a glance, then moved on. And holes are still dug in the lawn where a badger has probed for grubs.

Years ago, I might find wavy tracks in the grass and little black blobs of droppings: the distinctive trails of hedgehogs, now all gone. A few years ago, a farming friend brought me one of the creatures as a present. It had been annoying his daughter's dog by persistently turning up at night to lick its dish outside the kennel. Even tossed away on a fork it would come back. I released it gratefully into the grass but have seen no sign of it since. Should I blame the badger? In a study from England in 2014, a grassland area culled of badgers more than doubled its

Hedgehog, a most distinctive mammal

Oak hillside

hedgehogs over five years. Badgers are proved to eat hedgehogs occasionally, nosing inside their prickles, and do compete with them for food. But my suspicion is all there is.

Meanwhile, our single beech has grown bigger than we ever imagined, its branches curving down like a crinoline with the weight of foliage. Its pool of summer darkness has spread across the pond and sealed its decline with autumn's fall of bronzy leaves.

I miss the pond's life at every passing. When I made it, several decades ago, I used every care, bedding its professional plastic on soft sand from the shore. Filled from a hose and edged with flat rocks, it gleamed with promise. Eager, however, to 'take the bare look' off its plastic bottom, I sank a few shovelfuls of soil, a few buckets of plants from the lake with their attendant root and larvae. A few dollops of frogspawn from a pool up the hill and I thought I could sit back and wait for an ecosystem.

When the first fog of green algae had cleared, the pond soon came, indeed, to enchant our springs. Perhaps a hundred frogs clasped and churring in the water, their orgies piling it with spawn. A steeper sun discovered great water beetles gliding after tadpoles or the courtship ballet of gilded newts. At the surface, the scribbling of whirligig beetles, the dimpling of featherweight pond skaters, a first spring damselfly unfolding its crimson tinsel.

The plants competed with enthusiasm, jostling for sun. A yellow water lily stolen from a marsh eventually gave up its struggle for space as pondweeds, bogbean and water mint crowded together at the surface, and grasses and mosses crept in from the edge. The bogbean was a special delight in May and June, holding up pink-and-white flowers like fringed, orchidaceous hyacinths. They decorated, for a while, a pond that wanted so much to be a fen, if not, in some long, mossy future, a little bump of bog.

Frogs in mating embrace

I did fight this for a few years, laying into the pond each autumn with an ancient, long-handled, iron claw – the original muckrake – to drag out heaps of vegetation. These were duly left to drain so that accompanying creatures could hop, skip or slither back in. All I wanted was a little open water, some lively glitter and ripples, a bright mirror on dull days. But the effort finally was too much hard work, and natural succession has been left to take its course, hastened by the showering autumn leaves.

I have to forgive the beech: it has been great to live with, its growth astonishing since we brought it as a volunteer, half-metre 'whip' from a forest on a big estate. As with the oaks we grew from acorns, its first lesson was that trees start growing branches quite low down: it is only when these have been lopped off by people or chewed off by livestock that trees become the 'lollipop' shapes that children like to paint.

When the beech had hoisted up its branches from the ground, to the height of my shoulders, it occurred to me to try giving it a hug, as we 'greens' are commonly supposed to do. Wrapping my arms around its smooth, cool bark, I felt the sudden and startling communication of its massive and muscular strength and weight, its living otherness rooted in the soil. Everyone should do this at least once: the sensual shock is unique and revelatory.

In autumn, the beech puts up mushrooms in its shade, quite nondescriptly beige and uninviting as food. Or rather, it is the tree's underground, mycorrhizal network of fungi that raises the spore-laden fruit. The new, scientific attention to the 'wood wide web' of mycorrhizae has changed how we think of a forest.

The myriad fungal underground threads share nutrients with the trees and even link them for mutual care and nourishment. This rather suggests that a single beech could be lonely, but we only had room for one. Between the hug and the new meaning for its mushrooms, it has taken on a presence beyond mere beauty. With such new intuitions and understanding, we are closer to finding our role as one, remarkable species among the millions of the natural world.